"...And Of a Sound Mind"
(2 Timothy 1:7)

45 Tips and Teachings
On How to Ease
Depression

Burnett Eggleston

Burnett Eggleston

Published by BookBaby
7905 N. Crescent Blvd.
Pennsauken, NJ 08110

Scripture passages taken from NIV/KJV Parallel Bible: 1987
Fourth printing.
Zondervan Corporation

Cover idea by Jeff Eggleston
Cover design and creation by DATAFLOW CORP.
Book Format by Elizabeth Moro

Printed in the USA

Mobility

The days do not come easy
as my feet just trudge along
All melodies are absent
for me there is no song
The mood just lays dormant
the notes cannot be heard
They scream to be uncovered
They scream to be learned.

A ray of light has found me
Its warmth spreads deep and wide
The music flows so easily
No longer held inside
My song is hope for many
For I am not alone
The days they now come easy
My feet just dance along.

In Gratitude

I would like to dedicate "…And of a Sound Mind" to my husband. His steadfast love has carried me through many storms. He will forever be my lighthouse; up close and in the distance.

I love you madly.

Many thanks to Trina Vladescu who edited most of this book. She was always a breath of fresh air whenever we spoke. She gave constant reinforcement to my writing in the form of gingerly suggested improvements.

She is a treasure.

English Professor, Bob Mooney, helped with this book's creation when Trina was called away for family concerns. His experience as a teacher and author guided me to the finish line and bolstered my confidence along the way.

Thank you, Bob.

Elizabeth Moro brought "…And of a Sound Mind" to life as the book's interior formatter. She worked for months insuring an updated version was always accessible. She lent advice when she knew changes were important. She was always available when I needed a pep talk.

She is a treat.

Table of contents

"...And Of a Sound Mind"
(2 Timothy 1:7)

45 Tips and Teachings on How to Ease Depression

Introduction

We usually don't go looking for help until we need it. If it ain't broke, don't fix it.

If you are depressed while reading these tips and teachings, you may not "hear" all that is being said. A strong suggestion is to read through this book when feeling good also. The important words meant especially for you will find their way into your heart.

When you are feeling down, allow it. Try not to fight your depression. It's not a shameful feeling, it's a human feeling. Listen to others who have been there or are dealing with depression now. We are here to help one another......carry each other through life's storms. Remind yourself that the sun in your world will shine again.

Actually the sun is always shining; clouds are just in its way. The same is true for you. Above the gloomy clouds in your life is a vibrant, sunny you. Through the tips and teachings that lie ahead, you can rediscover healthy feelings and moods.

Managing those clouds will become an acquired skill. Watching them disappear at times, will be a joy.

There are many, many bright days ahead. Prepare to become the captain of your own soul. My hope is that you navigate through this little book with a hopeful heart and prepare to sail over calmer waters. You are at the helm; your choices lead the way.

On many pages of this book, "God" becomes a subject. The male pronouns, "He" and "Him" are used in this manner as an ease of expression. In no way am I defining God. God is a personal entity. Hold fast to your own relationship.

In the 1947 film, *It's a Wonderful Life*, two senior angels become aware of an earthling who is in deep trouble.[1] They call upon a novice angel named Clarence to journey to earth. His mission is to get Mr. George Bailey back on the road to sanity. If Clarence succeeds he earns his wings and becomes a full-fledged angel. He is chosen for the job because of his child-like faith.

Filled with compassion for the earthling, Clarence asks, "Is he sick?" "No," answers one of the angels, quite concerned. "Much worse. He's discouraged."

Now just how did George Bailey come to feel so desperate? He became this way when his co-worker, Uncle Billy, lost a large sum of money belonging to the bank that they both owned. Due to the discovered value of a life insurance policy, George came to believe he was worth more dead than alive. Enter: Clarence.

Discouragement can come and go. Discouragement can come and grow. Discouragement is a major component in the illness of depression.

In September of 1984, at the age of 30, I was a patient on a hospital psychiatric unit. I was definitely discouraged and deeply depressed.

During my inpatient stay, I was cared for by a kind and loving psychiatrist. He told me that severe depression was the worst pain known to mankind. I hugged him desperately and drenched his shoulder with my tears. Finally, someone understood the horror of my pain!

At age 29, I was married, and the mother of three little boys, four years old and younger.

I'd had a psychotic break six months earlier and tried to manage with tranquilizers, and talk therapy. I continued to work as a Special Education teacher but life became increasingly difficult. My nerves felt raw and I'd lost many of my defense mechanisms.

My fragmented mind left me with the inability to make and trust the smallest of decisions. The hospital provided a much needed time-out. I left with renewed hope and the realization that I had a lot of work to do. Little did I know it would be the first of many psychiatric admissions.

I was given the name of a top psychologist and psychiatrist. The three of us worked closely for many years. The origin of several negative experiences and feelings was revisited. We built upon my strengths and discovered new patterns of thinking. At times the work was grueling but the end of my therapy sessions were always a comfort. Frieda, my psychologist, knew that even adults love to be rocked while they are hugged.

I wrestled with many different levels of depression during these healing years. At times it was my friend. It told me there were important changes to be made in my life. It paved the way for realizing we always have the choice to see things differently. The power to change our mind is the greatest power we have.

Healing was enhanced by a wonderful support team: Clarence came in the form of my husband and sons, siblings, relatives, friends and local hospital staff. I was truly blessed.

Join me as I share life-giving tips and teachings for tackling depression.

Depression can present as mild to severe. To fully understand its complexities, I invite you to read the Diagnostic and Statistical Manual of Mental Disorders (DSM-5-5th edition) below.

"At least 5 of the following symptoms have to be present during the same 2-week period (and at least 1 of the symptoms must be diminished interest/pleasure or depressed mood) for a definition of clinical depression.

1) Depressed mood: For children and adolescents, this can also be an irritable mood.
2) Diminished interest or loss of pleasure in almost all activities (anhedonia).
3) Significant weight change or appetite disturbance: For children this can be a failure to achieve expected weight gain.
4) Sleep disturbance (insomnia or hyper-insomnia).
5) Psychomotor agitation or retardation.
6) Fatigue or loss of energy.
7) Feelings of worthlessness.
8) Diminished ability to think or concentrate; indecisiveness.

9) Recurrent thoughts of death, recurrent suicidal ideation without a specific plan, or a suicide attempt, or a specific plan for committing suicide.

Non-clinical depression is a normal reaction to painful life events and/or physical, mental and emotional stress." [2]

As can be imagined, depression batters the spirit. Sufferers describe feeling like their hearts are dragging on the floor. As they trudge through the day, they bruise them with each mechanical step. Their feelings of self-love, if present, are at an all-time low. They wonder: "Will I ever feel whole again?"

....*And Of a Sound Mind* offers a variety of ideas and suggestions for alleviating depressive pain. There is no order to the 45 Tips and Teachings. Whatever works at the time is the one to embrace. Only you know the extent of your suffering.

I have been blessed to find relief, comfort and healing in many methods this book has to offer.

The angel Clarence lovingly traveled to earth to help George Bailey re-discover his worth and sanity.

May the following pages serve as tools for your journey to ease depression. Let these words fortify your faith as you are filled with the gift of hope: "For God hath not given us the spirit of fear, but of power, of love, And of a Sound Mind." (2 Timothy 1:7)

(1)

Just Do It

When depression drains your energy and confines you to the couch, ask yourself this question: If I did feel good right now, what would I be doing? You might think, hmmm, gardening, going for a walk, going for a run, listening to music, or any favorite activity. Pick one and do it. Don't wait until you feel like doing it. Just do it. The feeling often follows the action. If this seems too daunting, promise yourself you are only going to spend 5 minutes on the activity. You can build up your time as you master strength.

Just put on those trusty 'ole sneakers and hit the pavement. Soon you'll get your body moving and a feeling of enjoyment just might catch up with you.

"Although no one can go back and make a brand new start,
anyone can start from now and make a brand new ending."
- Carl Bard

(2)

Don't Go it Alone

When mental clouds loom heavily, share your sadness with a trusted friend or loved one. Putting your feelings into words can purge the pain and purify thoughts and feelings.

Our God is a great listener. Give Him your thoughts and feel your heart grow lighter. God is......

Waiting for You
by Burnett Eggleston

When your heart feels so heavy
That no one's kind word
Can lift the dark burdens
Meant not to be heard

And hope seems to vanish
Leaving nothing to seize
But cold empty dreams
Blown amiss by the breeze

He knocks on the door
Of your soul, His home
And whispers, "My child,
You are never alone

I've been waiting for you
To comfort you so
Your troubles I'll carry
But please never go."

(3)

THOUGHTS PRODUCE CHEMICALS AND CHEMICALS PRODUCE THOUGHTS

Every thought creates some type of chemicals. The mood--lifting chemicals we most want in our brain are serotonin and dopamine. Positive thoughts create these chemicals. Serotonin and dopamine create these positive thoughts. We feel happy when these two chemicals are emitted, and flow through our brain.

"Gee my hair looks really nice today! "or "I love that neighbor of mine next door," are both thoughts that make you feel good inside. They are mood-boosting agents. You can sustain this mood through repetition of more positive thoughts.

Negative thoughts release a chemical called monoamine oxidase which lowers serotonin levels. We feel sad when this takes place.

"My friend is a jerk," or "I'll never be good at anything," are negative thoughts that can send our serotonin plummeting and lower our spirits.

Our job is to limit negative thinking and muster as many positive thoughts as we can.

How might we boost our serotonin and dopamine levels? A good place to start is with gratitude. It's impossible to be grateful and unhappy at the same time.

At the end of your day, jot down three things you are thankful for. Let your brain brim with positivity as they swim across your mind as you sleep.

Reread the gratitude list out loud to yourself in the morning.

Repeat this feel good process as often as you can. Add to the list of gratefulness. You are setting the stage for serotonin and dopamine to work their magic. Eliminate or reduce the creation of negative thoughts by practicing gratitude and let it pave the way to a peaceful day.

(4)

Color Me Happy

When we are depressed it's difficult to find beauty anywhere. The world looks drab and gray and anything but colorful. If a bright, yellow ray of sunshine does grace your view, bask in it. Let it draw you out of your pain, if only for a moment. The sun's bright hue can provide a welcomed warmth and wonder to a seemingly dismal day.

In a 2020 article by Cherry and Gans MD., the effects of color, as it impacts mood and behavior are examined.

The colors red, yellow, and orange are known as warm colors and evoke emotions ranging from feelings of warmth to feelings of anger and hostility.

The colors blue, green, and purple are known as cool colors. They are described as calming colors, but can also call to mind feelings of sadness or indifference. [3]

Experiment with colors and discover their effect on you. If red, yellow, and/or orange stimulate a warm, comforting feeling, splash them around your home. Maybe a new red throw rug will put a spring in your step. Try replacing wooden picture frames with shades of yellows and orange. See if brightening your surroundings brightens you too!

If any of the mentioned colors stir up hostile, sad, or indifferent feelings, decide if you want them in your home. They can be used to release anger by throwing such colored pillows around a room. Keep them in a spare bedroom and punch the daylights out of them. Give yourself permission to be angry and let them have it. Congratulate yourself for dealing with your angry feelings in a healthy way.

As reported, the colors blue, green, and purple can be calming. Place objects of these colors where they will catch your eye each day. How about light blue dishes that welcome you at each meal? A favorite purple sweater may have a soothing effect as it cradles you in comfort.

Go ahead and open yourself up to the wonderful world of color. Possibly replace your drab, gray surroundings with colorful rugs, frames, and dishes. Paint the walls you look at the most with an inviting tone. Enliven your home so it can enliven you.

(5)

GENERAL SELF-CARE

Depression often steals our desire to care for ourselves. We tend to eat too much or too little, throw exercise by the wayside, and showering becomes an overwhelming chore.

Commit to personal care every day. Brush those teeth and comb your hair. Splash some cool water on your face. Feel its refreshing power. If you can, make yourself bypass face-washing and go straight into the shower.

I've yet to talk to a depressed person who claimed a shower made them feel worse!

"Make happiness
a priority and be gentle
with yourself in
the process."
- Bronnie Ware

(6)

EXERCISE

Organizing a personal exercise regime can set you on the road to feeling better, physically and mentally. The amount or intensity of the exercise is not as important as the regularity. Consistency is the key. Pick an activity that stirs a bit of excitement within. Commit to a short amount of time. Five or ten minutes, every other day to begin with, and you're off. Floor exercises, walking, jumping a rope-anything that gets your blood flowing, can give a giant boost to your day!

Congratulations on making a good, healthy choice and seeing it through.

"An ant on the move does
more than a dozen ox."
- Lao Tzu

(7)

HEALTHY EATING

Sometimes the last thing we want to concentrate on when depressed is healthy eating. We aren't particularly keen on taking care of ourselves at the time so why bother? Ramen noodles would make a good start, with a pint of Häagen-Dazs as the main course!

Oh dear, what we feed our bodies can make a huge difference in our outlook on life.

Alice Gomstyn, in an article regarding food and mood, provides an interesting explanation.

There is a diet connection between what we eat and the emotions we feel. When healthy food is ingested good bacteria is created and fed to the brain. The brain and our gut work together to produce the feel good chemicals serotonin and dopamine. [4]

These two emotional energizers help us to enjoy life. Throw in a bunch of junk food and they will exit stage left.

A simple view of a complex process? Yes. Frankly, an article by Katherine Zeratsky reports the following:

People who ate a junk food diet consisting mainly of sweets, fried foods, and high-fat dairy, showed they suffered depression symptoms. She states that people who eat a diet rich in fruits, vegetables and fish have much less depression. [5]

During my depressive times, sugar was my biggest go-to food for comfort. It lifted me up for a while, but always dumped me in the doldrums.

It's an important food to limit in your diet. Be aware it has many aliases including fructose, sucrose, maltose, and dextrose. These are listed in the ingredients' section of food packages.

Most of us have a good idea of what constitutes a healthy way of eating: fresh fruits and vegetables, particularly berries and leafy greens, whole grains, beans, meat, cheese and eggs.

Some of the best foods to indulge in, when depressed include: walnuts, mushrooms, tomatoes, leafy greens, apples, beans, berries, avocados, and seeds. (i.e. sunflower seeds, pumpkin and sesame)

Enjoy your favorite foods but do not make sugar, processed foods, or starchy carbohydrates a mainstay of your diet.

And for an added tidbit-sugar is more addictive than cocaine!

(8)

MEDITATION

Though not always evident, the main goal of the *45 Tips and Teachings* is to live more fully in the present. The quest to reach this destination is particularly difficult to fulfill when we are depressed. So often we feel locked inside our own heads and can't get out. We hear people talk about the effects of tai chi, yoga and others on mindfulness. And yes, they are good. Allow me to expand on another.

Meditation is a method of relaxation that calms the body and mind. Let me introduce you to it by explaining what it's not.

According to Prevention magazine (6/19) there are 5 myths about meditation. I have taken the liberty to convey them as follows:

> **Myth #1**: *If you don't sit in a certain position you're doing it wrong.* You can be in many positions including standing up, lying on the floor, sitting in a chair, lying down, or moving.

The healing powers of meditation can even be enjoyed while showering, walking or commuting.

Myth #2: *You need to put a lot of time into it.* This just isn't so. It has been shown that 10 minute sessions can improve attention span and memory. Your brain can cope better with the complexities of life from even brief meditative periods. Like short periods of physical exercise, meditation's positive effects appear within minutes.

Myth #3: *You must be a spiritual person.* Many people think meditation is associated with religious and spiritual rituals, but truthfully, it's a secular way to promote focus, calm, and stilling of the mind.

Myth #4: *Some people just can't meditate.* If you can be with your thoughts for even a few minutes you can meditate. Begin by becoming aware of your breathing. Your thoughts are expected to exist. Let them come-don't invite them in for coffee-and let them go. Then return to your breathing. There's no way you can screw up. Each time your thoughts return, center yourself on your breathing.

Myth # 5: *You have to do it the right way.* There is no singular, correct way to meditate. You just want to discover the method with the most calming effects. You can try guided visualization which is a technique with a leader who helps you imagine yourself as extremely calm and relaxed. You can use the repetition of a mantra. A mantra is a certain word or phrase spoken aloud or silently.

You can use the mantra as you inhale and/or exhale during your breathing.

Meditation has the ability to reduce depression in many ways. A primary benefit is its ability to decrease inflammation by reducing chemicals caused by stress. [6]

By making meditation part of your routine, you are inviting serenity to serve as a faithful partner through life.

"Joy comes to us in ordinary moments.
We risk missing out when
we get too busy chasing down the extraordinary."

- Brene Brown

(9)

Get Your *ZZZZZZZZ*'s

The feeling of depression is exhausting in itself. Our mobility is often slower, and a general listlessness exists. Depressed people often report sleeping too much or too little. Mentally we can feel foggy and carry a general feeling of anxiety throughout the body. Being able to get and stay asleep is a monumental task.

The following is a list of good practices that promote sleep:

1. Only sleep and have sex in bed. Do not read or watch TV in bed.
2. Establish a consistent bedtime.
3. Do not eat or drink caffeinated products two hours before bedtime.
4. Turn off lights, TV, radio, and telephone.
5. Speak to your practitioner if you are on medication as some interfere with sleep.

Many people who don't experience sleep deprivation report enjoying calming activities before bedtime.

Reading, listening to meditation tapes or engaging in a relaxing card or board game, are but a few. We want to partake in present moment activities; chasing worry and concern away.

Two impressive and effective remedies for sleep are melatonin and lavender.

My daughter-in-law gave me a spritzer bottle of lavender to spray on my pillow at night. It induces a calming sensation and often times lulls me to sleep. One granddaughter takes a child's dose of melatonin and sleep for her comes quite quickly.

These and many other sleep agents can be found at grocery, drug, and health food stores anywhere.

The depressed person may have trouble concentrating. The increased inability to focus may also be a by-product of an antidepressant. Your mental health practitioner can help find a medication that works best for you.

When you are lying in bed at night, finding it hard to fall asleep, assure yourself that you are at least resting your body. This realization may bring comfort, ease anxiety, and even invite sleep.

(10)

EXPERT ADVICE

When depressive pain gets to be too much, you owe it to yourself to seek professional help. Your choice might be a social worker, psychologist, and/or a psychiatrist. Any mental health professional that you are comfortable with is a good start.

A good therapist is a trained, non-judgmental adult with an endearing capacity for unconditional love. Your session with this professional is usually 45 to 50 minutes. You will intrinsically know when you have found the right person for you. Usually you decide how often you will see them. If medication is needed your therapist can lead you to a credible professional.

A common subject worked on in therapy is anger. Anger turned inward can be a catalyst for depression. Often we feel we will lose the love of the person we are at odds with if we express our anger towards him. You and your therapist will skillfully uncover your buried pain. Like peeling an onion, you will slowly release past hurts and reconstruct a healthier state of being.

Be proud of yourself for seeking help. In the therapist's office it's all about you, and you will become better armed to face everyday life.

The most precious gift
We can offer anyone
Is our attention
When mindfulness
Embraces those we love
They will bloom like flowers. [7]

Thich Nhat Hahn

(11)

LIGHT AS A FEATHER

In the book, *The Four Agreements,* author Dom Ruiz gives us four "rules" for finding inner peace. Two of my favorites are, "Do not assume, and Take nothing personally.[8] When we assume, it feels like we are living inside another being's head. I say "being" because it could even be a pet. We find ourselves imagining what they are thinking and sometimes how they are feeling. We are often creating a scenario that most likely doesn't exist.

I sought the help of a therapist many times along my journey. One particular time I found that I could not get my mind out of my own children's heads. A couple of my sons were going through some particular struggles and my negative imaginings were increasing my own depression. They were grown adults who lived out of town and I mentally took up residence in their minds.

My therapist's response was brisk.

"What are you doing inside their heads!? You do not belong inside their heads! Those are their heads and you are trespassing! "She was so matter of fact, and abrupt that she shook the heck out of me. She definitely delivered the treatment I needed at the time. It was not long before I dropped assumptions and sheepishly returned to the moment at hand.

Occasionally I still find myself assuming what my kid's thoughts and feelings are. "You are trespassing!" bellows in my ears, as my wise therapist's voice shakes me into the present.

We have to catch ourselves in the act of making assumptions and consciously choose to drop them. This leads to a clear and healthier mind; a mind ready to enjoy what's going on around it.

Dropping assumptions is a lifetime practice. You know when you're able to do it. Your mind feels as light as a feather. A cool breeze ripples through your thoughts, chasing menacing ones away.

(12)

Do Not Take It Personally

A second tool from Don Luis is the ability to take nothing personally. An example of what this means is as follows:

I said hello to a co-worker I passed in the hall. She did not return the greeting. Immediately I internalized her silence and thought, "What's with her? Is she mad at me? What have I done to her? I'm not talking to her anymore."

When I took an inventory of how many times in an ordinary day I took someone personally, the answer was twelve!

In reality my colleague may not have heard me; she might have been deep in thought. Most likely her lack of response had nothing to do with me. As we can see, taking something personally can lead to nasty assumptions.

When we do take things personally, it almost always stirs up unpleasant feelings such as, hurt or anger. Remember anger turned inwards can deepen depression.

The wisest thing to do would be to remind yourself to take nothing personally, and remember the freeing feeling this provides. Drop the judgmental inner dialogue, and return to the present. I make this sound easy but it may be the hardest work you'll ever do.

A challenging example is when someone makes a negative remark about a person close to you...i.e. "Your brother is a jerk." No matter how hurtful this can be we are called to acknowledge the feelings, drop them, and carry on. Our head is clear to return to the moment. We are free.

The skill of taking nothing personally involves intense daily practice but the rewards are worth it. Your mind is now available to think constructively and a physical lightness envelops your head. You've freed yourself from the useless energy that preoccupation can drain. You can't put a price on a sound mind.

(13)

COME TO YOUR SENSES

When you find yourself feeling low and lost in a world of your own, try to activate one of your senses. Again, they are touch, taste, smell, hearing and vision. The goal is to bring your mind to what's going on in the present. For instance, tell yourself you're going to concentrate on your vision. Then direct your eyes to roam the surroundings. If you're outside, notice the deep blue color of the sky above. Watch it as it's peppered with sand-colored starlings, out-racing one another among the clouds. Perhaps you're standing in a grocery store line. Check out the different types of clothing attire on those around you. If home is where you are, let your eyes soak in the variety of colors, shapes, and sizes of the furniture that adorns each room.

When possible, light a scented candle, close your eyes, and just take in the aroma. Inhale deeply and feel the relief as menacing thoughts begin to slip away. Gradually work with the other senses and let each one bring you back to the present.

Only you know the stress and pain your world has held. Accentuate that sense that's likely to bring the most comfort.

"You are the sky.
Everything else is just the weather."
- Pema Chodron

(14)

A SOUL ENLIGHTENED

Have you ever read or heard a person's words that changed your life forever? It was May of 2012 when such an experience happened to me.

While working as a busy Chaplain I found I needed a shot in the arm concerning my faith. A 2010 book, *Rediscover Catholicism* by Matthew Kelly, gave me that boost.[9] It created in me a desire to seek the sacrament of Reconciliation. This sacrament involves meeting with a Catholic priest and telling him your sins, that he might forgive them. It usually ends with absolution of those sins, a contrite heart as professed in a prayer called The Act of Contrition, and an act of penance. I went to the church located in the neighborhood where I grew up and sat in a room with a very lovely priest. I told him it had been quite a while since I had been to Confession (the old term) and he just smiled. For about 10 minutes I told Father the things I was sorry I did and did not do. He listened intently and his soft eyes seemed to say "go on." When I was finally quiet he spoke these words:

"God does not care about one thing you have said here today. All God wants for you is that, while you're on this earth, you find inner peace. Have a good day."

Was this a typical Reconciliation experience? I don't know. Priests and parishioners are all different. It was important to me at the time and lifted me out of a deep sadness.

I summed up my meeting with Father in these words: "Our God is a gentle God. His will is that we be happy. Find your passion, and treat yourself lovingly." Father's words found a way to my soul. I felt a wave of this inner peace.

(15)

REST IS A GIFT

Many of us were brought up to feel that we had to "earn our keep" or prove our worth by being productive. A common parental command around our house was, "make yourself useful." I am one of eleven children whose dad at times held down five jobs. When he was home I felt like I had better be busy or make sure I looked busy. When he walked into the kitchen I would grab silverware and pretend to polish it. This always felt awkward since it wasn't even silver. Honestly it was easier to BE busy then to try to look busy.

The idea of feeling like we constantly have to be productive is one that I would like to lay to rest.

We are loved by our God for just BEING. We are wonderful in God's eyes just by merely existing. We do not have to "do" anything to bask in the love of God.

Depression often steals our ambition. This is part of the illness and it's ok.

As humans it is enjoyable and satisfying to complete tasks and feel "useful." When we feel better we do better. Beating ourselves up in between will increase our sadness. A healthy balance of rest and activity will restore a feeling of groundedness. Once again the times when we have little get-up -and -go, can remind us that our job, for now, is to just BE.

Acceptance of this current state can ready us for an ascent to a higher level of understanding-an understanding of the feeling of self-love.

During a certain period in my life I struggled with a horrible lack of ambition and self-understanding. I felt useless and without direction of any kind. This poem manifested, and a question harbored within.

Be
by Burnett Eggleston

Be---Me.
A me I've never known before
and can't describe to others
in a way they'll understand.

The struggle is so lonely.

A fight I've never fought before
and don't even care to win.

I am coming into being
and the birth is still exciting
fires rage inside me
and yet I feel no pain.

To silence this quiet burning
seems to me a crime

Where must I go to shine?

The path of beingness had stirred up a fire within. It lead me to pursue writing. After you have endured the feeling of just "being", a path to follow may come into sight. Yes, to rest is a gift but there will come a time when your energy returns. Out of the stillness a new direction may emerge. What passion lays dormant in your soul?

"A few simple tips for life: feet on the ground,
head to the skies, heart open, quiet mind."
- Rasheed Ogunlaru

(16)

I BELIEVE IN ME

I think we can agree that accomplishing tasks makes most of us feel good. Depression will not let us engage in much and sometimes even simple routine tasks such as brushing our teeth is a pain. Darkness can fill the mind, blinding our ability to recognize doable things. Chipping away at very small tasks can restore our sense of self-worth and meaning.

Ask yourself, "What can I achieve today that will make me proud of myself at the end of the day?" It can be the smallest of things. When we have succeeded at several different small activities, we might try to accomplish bigger ones.

Make a small list of simple tasks before bed. In the morning pick one and complete it. At the day's end you will feel a sense of pride that comes from keeping your word. After a while you'll be able to add more activities to the list.

The main goal of this activity is to increase your integrity. You deserve to believe in yourself. The more promises you keep the more faith you will have in YOU.

"Much of our spiritual life
is self-acceptance,
maybe all of it."
- Jack Kornfield

(17)

Strength in Numbers

Do you know people that just always seem happy? No matter what's going on in the world, these people are smiling. I'm not condemning them, though I do admit I feel a bit jealous. I think it's very possible they have their bad days too. I'll tell you why in a minute.

To have and feel many moods and emotions is part of the human condition. It is the duration and intensity of some of these moods that may bring us down and make it difficult to cope and function effectively. When we get tired of going it alone, it might be helpful to consider joining a support group. Your therapist, church, or Mental Health Organization may be able to lead you to a relevant support group and its meeting time and place.

Some of the benefits of a support group are:
- o   Attendance is not mandatory.
- o   You are likely to make a friend or two.
- o   You might feel a sense of community.
- o   You might discover that you are not alone.
- o   You can compare different health regimes with other participants.

- The leader will most likely "pull" from you things like, "the best thing that happened this week?" etc...

I led a support group for many years. Two of those people we talked about above who are always smiling, were loyal members.

"Fight for the things you care about,

but do it in a way that will lead others to join you."

- RBG

(18)

ONLY ONE OF YOU

I have had the privilege of counselling many patients who were hospitalized with depression. Many were there because they tried to take their life. So often their lack of self-love and self-worth was evident. They spoke negatively about themselves and rarely looked you in the eye when they communicated.

Initially I tried to be supportive towards what they were going through. Next I found these challenging words of mine to be very helpful:

You are a creation of God. Who are you to destroy his handwork?

Your life does not belong to you alone. You are a part of all your relatives and friends....and people you don't even know.

There is only ONE of you in this world. There's been no one like you and there never will be again. You are unique!

If you ponder things slowly, you will be in less pain.

Hug the four year old inside of you and let him/her know everything's going to be ok.

To like one's self.......a daily mission. To love one's self ....a divine goal.

Let your divinity shine!

"Loving ourselves through the process of owning our own story

is the bravest thing we can do."

- Brene Brown

(19)

"...TOMORROW WILL WORRY ABOUT ITSELF."
(Matthew 6:34)

I have talked repeatedly about practicing the present; getting our mind into where we are and what we're doing. Some days this is a loftier goal than others.

Sometimes I am depressed and preoccupied. For instance, when one of my sons is facing a serious challenge, my mind continuously leaps into the future and expects the worse. This is due to making assumptions. I find my thinking is full of "what-ifs" and I am unable to focus on the present MOMENT.

I recently told myself to temporarily forget trying to live in the present. Strive to just live in the present DAY! (i.e., Monday, Tuesday, etc.) I give myself permission to be concerned about things going on only in the present DAY. When my mind jumps forward to future days, and I feel anxious, I gently remind myself to stay grounded in whatever day it is.......and think ONLY about that day.

I am being a bit repetitive here for a purpose. Some days it is just too hard to stay in the present moment. So cut yourself some slack and try to confine your thoughts to the day at hand.

A helpful technique is to repeat the day of the week when your mind starts to wander. "Today is Wednesday. Today is Wednesday. I am thinking about only Wednesday."

If you get up in the morning and say, "I am going to fall down today". Chances are you will fall down. We want our days to be filled with the expectation of good. And if you teach yourself to handle one day at a time, goodness will grow throughout that day.

You are the artist in your world and expectation is your tool of expression. Make it a beautiful day!

(20)

I Like Me

The emphasis of this exercise is to help us see ourselves in a positive light. Create a list of at least five things you like about you. Ask yourself such questions as, "Is there a certain body part I like?" "Do I have any talents?" "Am I a kind person?"

This can be difficult as no one is harder on ourselves than we.

Start and end your day by reading your list. Rather than remotely going through it, picture what you are saying. If you find you have beautiful hair, see in your mind it's color, style and texture. Feel the pride you have in possessing such a lovely feature. Continue this process with each item on the list.

Start and end your day for at least a couple of weeks with this habit. By believing in the positive qualities that you possess, you will boost your self-esteem and grow stronger in the salvation of self-love.

It is up to us, and God, if God is invited, to change the lenses we see ourselves through.

We all possess beautiful features and qualities. It is up to us to own them, accentuate them, and love them.

Let positivity possess our souls as we produce a healthier self-image.

And don't forget the good chemicals we are creating in our brains!

(21)

BELIEF IN BELIEF

God heals through science and faith. With the power of God within them, scientists create a pill or remedy and the patient has faith it will work. Is that all there is to it?

What if the patient doesn't have a belief in the medicine and the medicine still works? This is a quandary. My answer is that, maybe the medicine activates the area of the brain that generates faith, and faith is involved unconsciously.

There exists a wonderful book called *The Mists of Avalon*, by Marion Zimmer Bradley.

> *The mists of Avalon are a mythical illusion to the tales of King Arthur. Avalon is a magical island that is hidden behind huge impenetrable mists. Unless the mists part, there is no way to navigate your way to the island. But unless you believe the island is there, the mists won't part.* [10]

Oh how powerful belief can be!

In some of the earlier Tips and Teachings, we examined how antidepressants can be mood boosting and/or mood stabilizing. How much of their positive effects are the result of positive expectation? In a study reported by F. Zeidan, it showed that MRI scans revealed that brain pain networks responded according to the expectations of the majority of study participants! [11]

Am I suggesting we forego medicine and rely totally on the power of belief? Absolutely not. It only makes sense that we would take advantage of both. My feeling is that faith is extremely powerful and can synthesize processes that activate the power of the remedy. I think it may fortify the properties of the medicine and release positive chemicals within the brain that aid in healings and cures.

(22)

CLICK CLICK

I have always touted the relaxation effects of knitting. While researching this phenomenon I found a study that backs me up. A reporter for Prevention magazine, (6/19) tells us "...in a study of more than 3500 knitters, 81% felt happier and calmer after clicking their needles…...repetitive negative thoughts were curbed." Little room was left for depressive thoughts. [12]

Other needlecrafts can be soothing and evoke a relaxation response also. But it is the act of knitting, which includes the clicking of the needles, that stimulates the calming effects and leaves you feeling happier.

Many craft stores offer knitting classes that range from beginner to advanced. I learned to knit when I was ten. A dear aunt taught me the skill. It has been one of my main hobbies and saving interests ever since.

A little break for your reading enjoyment:

Therapist

Tell me what I want to hear
I'm paying you a bunch
Don't sit there in silence
I might as well get lunch.

Alright alright I'll say something
Please promise not to judge
The words just don't come easy
Like a term paper that's fudged.

I don't know how to trust you
You haven't said a word
If I pour my heart out
Please show me I am heard.

Ok I'm ready to begin
so sorry for my brew
I don't know why I'm sitting here
My childhood was good!

(23)

HAHAHAHAHA

During a mild depression of low energy, negative outlook, and just plain miserableness, I realized I hadn't laughed in weeks. I knew this wasn't good. I googled "jokes" on my phone and discovered a variety of funny material. I sat and read several good-humored pieces and found myself laughing within minutes.

How did I start to feel better so quickly?

When we laugh our brain releases endorphins which are feel-good chemicals.

They can even relax our muscles so much that we literally fall right out of our chair laughing. People are known to wet their pants during a good laugh.

Have you ever found yourself laughing at something on an elevator with someone you've never met? Doesn't it feel great? Laughter is truly cosmic glue.

You can laugh with anyone in the whole world and within seconds you feel closer. You can even have a good guffaw with chimps.

Other cheerful-chuckles might be found by watching a stand-up comedian on YouTube, tuning into a comedy movie and/or purchasing a joke book and vowing to read a page a day.

Your immune system is weakened by depression. Laughter fortifies it. It helps you to focus, feel balanced, and release anger. It even enables you to forgive.

For more wonderful benefits of laughter see Annette Goodheart's *Laugh Your Way to Health* video.(1985) [13] She defines laughter as …...cosmic juice.

(24)

SAY "CHEESE"

The last thing we feel like doing when feeling low is "smiling". But there are huge benefits to this simple act of, sometimes, faked expression. In a study by SCL Health, it was shown that smiling releases endorphins, natural painkillers, and serotonin."[14] These three neurotransmitters can make us feel good inside and out.

As with laughter, these natural chemicals boost your mood, relax your muscles and reduce mental and physical pain.

Smiling is not simply a physical reaction but also a conscious choice. There is strong evidence that smiling leads to good health, and overall longevity.

According to a current article on happiness, M. Stibich gives us ten good reasons to smile every day:

> - *Smiling helps you live longer.*
> - *Smiling relieves stress.*
> - *Smiling elevates our mood.*
> - *Smiling is contagious.*
> - *Smiling boosts your immune system.*
> - *Smiling lowers your blood pressure.*
> - *Smiling reduces pain.*
> - *Smiling makes you more attractive.*
> - *Smiling makes you seem successful.*
> - *Smiling helps you stay positive.* [15]

When you smile your stomach physically relaxes. You can feel this as it happens.

A smile on our face not only affects us positively, but also those around us.

God knows how difficult it is to smile when you're feeling low. Keep in mind earlier advice from Tip #1: Just do it. Cheerfulness might just take over as your smile spreads happiness to others.

"Say Cheese."

(25)

DWELLING

Dwelling involves having perseverating thoughts that just won't go away. Sometimes they are painful, worrisome thoughts. Often times they accompany depression. We ruminate on the same mental material. A thought appears and circulates over and over in our head. As a result it is difficult to engage in healthy ones. This process can physically cause debilitating headaches. Ouch!

What can we do to stop? First of all we must make ourselves aware of the fact that we are doing it. We are thinking about the same thing, over and over again. A tense or numb feeling can be present in our head, and signal to us that we are caught in a ditch of dwelling. It is then that we tell ourselves to shift gears. Go on to a new, pleasant thought. This isn't easy but with practice it can be done.

We want to develop a strong command over our thoughts. One of the kindest things we can do for ourselves is to pay gentle attention to what we are thinking.

Accept our thoughts as they arise and steer them in a healthy direction. Bring them back to the present where they focus on the here and now. You will feel a deep sense of peace.

Learning to be masters of our own mind is a lifelong endeavor. It is a feat so worth pursuing. Complete control of the human mind is achieved by few.

(26)

ECT

Electroconvulsive therapy (ECT) is a procedure that offers hope and healing to those who are not getting better from therapies and medications. Its usage is highly beneficial to schizophrenic individuals, treatment-resistant bipolar patients, and the severely depressed.

Just what is ECT?

ECT is a treatment whereby electricity is used to induce a short seizure in the brain while a patient is under anesthesia. The scientific explanation of the treatment is extensive. In short a brief seizure is initiated in the brain that stimulates feel good chemicals such as dopamine and serotonin. A psychiatrist orders ECT with the patient's permission. It is done with hospitalized patients and is also administered on an out-patient basis.

The facts I present here are taken from my own experience with ECT, in an upstate, New York hospital. However, a friend who is presently having the procedure in central Florida, reports almost identical protocols.

ECT is generally given before breakfast. As stated it involves anesthesia and the stomach must be empty. A psychiatrist, nurse, and psychiatric technician are among the treatment team present.

Prior to the procedure the patient fills out a thorough description of how he is feeling. This provides a comparison for the doctor as to the effectiveness of the ECT, from treatment to treatment.

One treatment is given on any certain day. The treatment takes about 15-20 mins and recovery is 20-30 mins. The helpful effects are usually short term so most often additional treatments are needed. Their effectiveness builds upon one another. ECT is often given two to three times a week, for a few weeks. However there are people who have found significant relief from just one or two treatments.

Memory loss can be a side effect of ECT. Usually it is temporary but some loss can be permanent. During my history of depression I found solace and pain relief in ECT. My mood gradually lifted and I developed an overall feeling of well-being. I felt energetic once again and looked forward to each day. I experienced some memory loss but nothing disturbing. For example, I found I could remember only one way to get to a destination when prior I knew of many. This gradually improved.

One needs to ask their self, "Am I willing to let go of some old memories, to feel good enough to make new ones?" By this I mean ECT can lift your depression allowing you to live more fully in the present.

The effectiveness of ECT does not decrease with age. For the elderly, it is even found to be better than pharmacology.[16]

It is one of the fastest treatments for severe depression and suicidal patients.

"Emancipate yourself from mental slavery,
none but ourselves can free our mind."

- Bob Marley

(27)

BOW-WOW/MEOW

Pets can be very therapeutic for our mental health. Dogs and cats are champions at minimizing loneliness and encouraging exercise and high-spirited fun. They are even a factor in improved vascular health.

From what I've witnessed children who grow up with and care for an animal may be more confident, active, and secure.

To love an animal and feel it's unconditional love, can open one's heart to life-giving pleasure. It can lift your spirits momentarily or for hours at a time. Just the act of sending out love and feeling its reciprocation gives added meaning to our lives.

Dogs and cats are not the only animals that can bring you joy. Guinea pigs, birds, fish and many pets may increase your happiness and sense of purpose.

The act of caring for a pet: feeding it, cleaning it, holding it, can put your troubles on the back burner. Pets can be faithful friends and enrich your soul with joy.

"The meeting of two personalities is like
the contact of two chemical substances;
if there is any reaction, both are transformed."

- Carl Jung

(28)

HOSPITALIZATION

Locked in. Frightened. Get me out of here. Now!!!

Or.........thank heaven I'm here. I feel so safe.

Or.........I'm frightened to be here but I'm so glad that I am.

Being hospitalized for mental illness can make you feel like a failure. The feeling of being stigmatized looms heavily. Shame can fill your soul.

Sometimes these feelings lay dormant the first few days of your stay. You may be in a mental fog when you enter the hospital. Often times you don't remember being admitted. Deep down you know you are feeling ungrounded. Your loved ones and your Dr. or therapist have noticed your emotional fragility. A choice has been made by you or for you (depending on your age) to seek a more secure setting. (Age 21 brings your own power of consent.) Relief washes over those that care about you.

Life has become overwhelming. You need help to get better. Your safety and possibly the safety of others are at stake.

You have entered a secure unit, designed to rebalance and bring about a healthier state of mind.

In the very beginning of this book I shared the experience of being hospitalized at age 30. (That was 30 some years ago) The embarrassment I felt was excruciating at the time. My favorite uncle showed up to visit and I was so confused. For some reason I thought because I was locked in, visitors were locked out. I don't know why I thought this. I felt a complete prisoner of my own mind.

"How did you know I was here?" I asked my uncle.

"You can't drop out of YOUR social circle unnoticed," he teased.

Oh God, I thought. Others must know I'm here too! The thought was unbearable.

Growing up, if anyone was known to have mental or emotional troubles, they were said to "have problems." "Don't listen to her......she "'has problems," and "he doesn't know what he's talking about, "he has problems," were common remarks.

Finding myself in a hospital, confirmed to me, that I too "had problems." My worst fear had come true. I felt I would never be believed again! The thought was horrifying. I was overcome with terror at its possibility.

The cloudy state of mind cleared within a couple of days. I faced the truth. I was a patient on a hospital, psychiatric unit. I could no longer come and go. My illness had made me a prisoner in more ways than one.

(29)

HOSPITALIZATION II

Finding myself one of many patients brought me comfort. So often during my illness I felt gravely alone. In the hospital I met several patients of all different ages dealing with life issues.

I was assigned a psychiatrist who led a treatment team of nurses, aides, technicians, social workers, therapists, and other medical staff. There were healing groups offered that addressed the body, mind, and spirit. You were not forced to attend but highly encouraged. Your doctor often viewed your attendance as a sign of your growing self-help and optimism.

Some of the groups included cognitive behavioral therapy, a therapy designed to highlight and change negative thought patterns as they affect depression and other emotional issues. Art therapy invited emotional expression through different modalities. Acrylic paints, water colors, and clay were very popular. Music therapy involved singing, brief guitar and piano lessons and just plain being present as others took part. Attendance was warranted though staying in your room was such an incredible lure.

A spirituality class was offered whereby a Chaplain presented rich, and inspiring material. Her handouts were always shared and saving was encouraged.

One favorite saying was, "If you're having trouble finding God, get in the present moment and God will find you." Chaplain Barb wrote this one herself and exclaimed it was her favorite too!

Sometimes one spoken nugget could make your day more bearable.

My hospital stay provided many tools for facing and solving problems. Medications were adjusted and continued therapy was encouraged. The cloistered setting slowed me down, and helped me to focus. The hospital experience gave me the aid I needed to, once again engage with other people. It shined a light on problems yet to be tackled. I met new friends learning to face their problems too.

The staff were exceptionally compassionate!

I had a lot of work to do. I felt newly-found energy to do it.

The mission of this energy was to help me live in the present.

My ultimate goal was self-acceptance and learning to love myself -well.

(30)

HOPE

The following is a story to lift your spirits. Its author is Loren Eisley.

As the old man walked the beach at dawn, he noticed a young man ahead of him picking up starfish and flinging them into the sea.

Finally catching up with the youth, he asked him why he was doing this. The answer was that the stranded starfish would die if left until the morning sun.

"But the beach goes on for miles and there are millions of starfish," countered the other. "How can your effort make any difference?"

The young man looked at the starfish in his hand and then threw it to safety in the waves. "It makes a difference to this one," he said. [17]

One act of kindness can go a long way. Little by little they add up. Significance does not lie in numbers. It lies in action. It lies in love.

A pleasant fact: Kindness given, received and witnessed is known to increase your serotonin levels thus lifting your mood.

"So we shall let the reader answer this question for himself:

Who is the happier man,

he who has braved the storm of life and lived or

he who has stayed securely on shore and merely existed?"

- Hunter S. Thompson

(31)

TEAMING UP

The importance of medication during your journey through depression cannot be overstated. Is it for everyone? No. Would I say it's vital for many people? Yes, maybe even most. I'm not going to list the eons of medicinal and homeopathic aids available. They can be found on the internet quicker than I can review them.

The current mode of treatment is medication management rather than dispense and withdraw. For many patients, this seems to be the best path.

I want to emphasize again that we are walking chemicals and it's a chemical balance that we are pursuing. We can achieve this balance through talk therapy alone. But, like slicing that onion, we want to limit the tears. Medicine, in its different forms, can help tremendously to ease our pain. Like talk therapy medicine can enhance cognitive clarity, resulting in increased problem-solving ability, and help with managing your moods.

Teaming up talk therapy with medicine, again, is often a winning combination.

"Wisdom says we are nothing. Love says we are everything.
Between these two, our life flows."

- Jack Kornfield

(32)

COMPLETE

I bring this subject to the forefront because I've tackled it most of my life.

It's a feeling that no one can directly give you. You have to experience it for yourself. Yes, a loving childhood environment can nurture it's growth but this is not always the case. It's also a feeling that can come and go. You will know when it's here to stay.

WORTHINESS. It comes when you are able to accept yourself for who you are and love yourself unconditionally. It can be a difficult pursuit but a goal WORTH achieving.

"Happiness is having a large, loving, caring, close-knit family in another city."

- George Burns

(33)

COMFORTABLE WITH WHO WE ARE

At times, life can be an insidious struggle to find the answer to just "who we are." This mystery can be a plague that comes and goes, usually during negative experiences. Depression can harbor such experiences. How do we know when we have arrived at the answer? The following offers a momentous clue:

> "When you are truly
> Comfortable with
> Who you are
>
> Not everyone will
> Like you
>
> But you won't care
> A bit." [19]

Self-acceptance is a wonderful state that will carry you to heights you could never have imagined. It is a dynamic process that demands interior reflection and consistent examination of one's world and reaction to it. Forgiveness is a major component of it; forgiveness of self and others.

"Many people think excitement is happiness.
But when you are excited, you are not peaceful.
True happiness is based on peace."

- Thich Nhat Hanh

(34)

EXCELLENCE

In groups I use to lead on psychiatric units I would ask the question, "Who thinks they are a perfectionist?" Very few hands went up. I then explained that a perfectionist feels that things and even themselves are never good enough or perfect enough. Then several hands went up.

We discussed the difference in perfectionism and excellence with excellence being our goal. The following, is a dynamic comparison of excellence and perfection:

"Excellence is willing to be wrong;
Perfection is being right.
Excellence is risk;
Perfection is fear.
Excellence is powerful;
Perfection is anger and frustration.
Excellence is spontaneous;
Perfection is control.
Excellence is accepting;
Perfection is judgment.
Excellence is giving;
Perfection is taking.

Excellence is confidence;
Perfection is doubt.
Excellence is flowing;
Perfection is pressure.
Excellence is journey;
Perfection is destination." [18]

Setting the bar too high for ourselves can make life unbearable. Aim for "good enough" and excellence may develop.

Perfection is not for humans to achieve. Its pursuit can be painful. Let excellence lead the way. Aim for progress not perfection.

(35)

"...As We Forgive Those..."

Forgiveness. For...give...ness. It is a gift we give ourselves more than the person we forgive. It unshackles the chains that bind us- the chains of anger, hurt, judgment, revenge and ill will.

Alexander Pope gave us the saying, "to err is human to forgive is divine." [20] The first part we know is easy. We are all victims of wrong-doing. To forgive ourselves and those who've offended us, is often an insurmountable feat. But, as stated, it frees us from the clutches of the past and allows us to go forward.

Forgiveness releases our spirit from bondage; our soul is no longer held captive and tossing in a sea of suffering.

I do believe we came to earth to manifest our divinity. Practicing forgiveness is the key.

Forgiveness can be a lengthy venture. Being willing to forgive does not automatically make it happen.

When our hearts and minds entwine in love towards those we are at variance, forgiveness can be born.

Gerald G Jampolsky, MD, offers us a *Prescription for Peace*:

Forgive our parents totally.

*Forgive everyone who has ever been here, who is here now, or
who will ever be here, including ourselves, totally.*

Forgive the world totally.

Forgive God totally.

Take a leap of faith and trust in love, trust in God.

Choose to experience peace rather than conflict.

Choose to experience love rather than fear.

Choose to be a love finder rather than a fault finder.

Choose to be a love giver rather than a love seeker.

Teach only love.[21]

Close your eyes. Wrap your arms around yourself and comfort and forgive the child within. Hear the chains as they fall to the floor. Smile and see the smiles of those you've forgiven. Come together and breathe a deep sigh of relief. The past is gone. It is no more.

The Light within us shines a new beginning. Love, once again, leads the way.

(36)

THE SPIRITUAL JOURNEY

To love ourselves is a human longing. We yearn for it in our bones. The search for it demands an acceptance of one's thoughts and feelings. One's spirit affirms its existence. On a deeper level, it encaptures our soul. When we feel love for ourselves we more easily feel love for others. When we find this love, we feel whole.

The absence of self-love creates a void.... a gaping space we are constantly trying to fill.

It seems that maybe acting from a kind heart would invite its existence, but this is not the case. This is not enough.

We brim with self-love by caring for ourselves in this unique way:

"And then I learned the spiritual journey had nothing to do with being nice. It was about being real, authentic. Having boundaries.

Honoring my space first, others second. And in this space of self-care, being nice just happened. It flowed not motivated by fear, but by love." [22]

"The journey IS the destination, enjoy the ride"

- Burnett Eggleston, Jr.

(37)

PRAYERSCRIPTIONS

I have been a Chaplain at a local hospital for over ten years. I had the privilege of counseling patients who were in various stages of depression. Distributing uplifting literature was a favorite pastime. At one point a new policy was enforced on the units. Anything with staples was not allowed to be shared with the patients. Staples were deemed a danger.

I had a favorite little paperback with 40 biblical verses-each expounded upon in simple, comforting language. And aha, it had staples!

I cut each page out of the "book." We have a wonderful graphic arts department at the hospital. They took each page and adorned the front with beautiful, meaningful artwork. The flipside of the now staple-free "card" contained a scriptural passage and a joyful and optimistic message. I called each creation a "prayerscription."

The title of this book: *"And of a Sound Mind"* was taken from one of the prayerscriptions: "For God hath not given us the spirit of fear, but of power, of love, and of a sound mind. "(2 Timothy 1:7)

The following paragraphs are written on this card:

"Your fears can be healed by this text. It tells us, first, that fear is overcome by power. What power? There is only one force more powerful than fear, and that is faith. When fear comes to our mind, counter it with an affirmation of faith.

Second, love overcomes fear. By love is meant trust, confidence, and complete dependence upon God. Practice this attitude and fear will diminish. The third element is to attain a sound mind in which there are no complexes, quirks and obsessions. Live with the thought of God, and you will develop a sound mind where no shadowy fear can lurk.

Whenever you are afraid, verbalize against the thing you fear, using the words of this text. " [23]

When I visited with patients and handed out my "prayerscription," I would teasingly say, "Now read this 3x a day, with or without food. So far no one has complained of any allergic reactions to this healing verse, so you should be all set."

There were many times when I was able to see a patient only once. My inspirational cards served as shortcuts to providing people with compassionate support.

*"I shall lead you
through the loneliness,
the solitude
you will not understand;
but it is My shortcut
to your soul. "*

T. Merton [24]

"Ya Gotta Believe"

- Tug McGraw

(38)

OUR PURPOSE

Very often when we are depressed and even when we aren't, we find ourselves entertaining some very deep questions. Examples might be, "What is my purpose in life?" and, "How will I know when I have found it? "

The answers do not have to be complicated. What if God's only will for us is that we be happy? I have read this in many places over the years. A few years ago it finally seemed to sink in. God radiates through us when we are happy. Why wouldn't He wish this state of mind for all of us?

Our mission is to discover what makes us profoundly happy. When we find it we will have found our purpose. Being a wife and a mother, or a husband and a dad, might serve as one's happiness. But what if you're crazy about the job you have too? There is no limit on the sources of your happiness. They can all feed into your purposeful life.

In Teaching #14, A Soul Enlightened, the Catholic priest relates that God's only purpose for us is that we find inner peace. Complete happiness and inner peace, I would deem as one and the same.

Many people do not inherently believe that they deserve to be happy. In Tip# 31, we talk about worthiness. You cannot find your bliss if you don't think you deserve to. This is a common dilemma when searching for your purpose. You block its manifestation by believing you aren't good enough…...good enough to be happy.

You must feel entitled to happiness for it to find you. You attract it by your mode of thinking and being. Being happy is a decision. Love yourself and the world will love you back. Profound happiness is your birthright!

(39)

RENEWED

In Psalm 51:10 in the bible, we read, "Renew a right spirit within me." This verse insinuates that we did possess a right spirit at one time and somehow lost it. Different hardships such as deep losses, abusive relationships, addictions and other traumatic occurrences can be responsible. Our pain can be so deep that we've lost touch with what a "right" spirit feels like.

A right spirit has to do with what's called disposition. Disposition can be described as one's temperament and behavior manifested toward situations and people. If we act negatively- cranky, cross, snappy, and/or disagreeable in our daily lives, it can ruin our relationships.

When we suffer from depression it is easy to have a poor disposition. We feel so miserable and stifled that the good happening around us isn't apparent. We are seeing through a clouded lens and carrying a heavy heart. It is common to relate poorly to others when the sun is shining but impossible to detect.

God, our creator, can help restore a right spirit within us. He is a master at bringing balance into our lives. We need to ask Him in faith, to walk beside us, and work with us. Our job is to ask Him several times a day to, "Renew a right spirit within us, " We then enact such feelings as cheerfulness, generosity, love and joy.

Imagine positive feelings washing over you. Feel a sense of calm claiming your spirit. Take a deep breath and trust that you are going to feel better and better. When negative feelings creep back, visualize an ocean tide sweeping them out to sea, erasing them from the shores of your mind.

Together with God you have, "Renewed a right spirit within you. (me)"

(40)

COMPLETE NOT COMMIT

A common symptom of severe lows is a preoccupation with death. This can lead to thoughts about God and the graveness of taking one's life. Many of us have been in this kind of darkness. Sometimes we feel we have put our family through enough, or the overall mental pain is more than we can bear. For many, their religion condemns suicide and teaches eternal damnation will follow. While unaware of all religious teachings, I know the Catholic Church believes that taking one's life is not a sin. The current belief is that a person is not in their right mind when they end their life. It's not a sane action.

When I was in graduate school for social work, one professor spoke about a movement to rename the phrase "committing suicide." The belief was that the word "commit" inferred a crime and suicide was no longer viewed as such. The hope was that "completed" suicide would replace "committed" suicide. I don't know how widespread the discussion became back in the 2000's, but the term has yet to grow popular within the public domain. I, though, prefer to use the term "completed."

With thoughts of death come ideas about God. In this book's introduction it was explained that the male pronouns, Him and He, would stand for God. No general definition would be offered. Everyone is to identify with their own meaning of God. Hold tight to who God is to you. Sometimes the less we try to identify God, the more real God can become to us.

I believe God is the God of the living, and has nothing to do with death. We die because of sicknesses, diseases, accidents, and natural causes. My feeling is that God does not call us or take us out of this world. Because God resides within us, God accompanies us at the time of death. As we take our last breath our braided spirits journey from this life to the next. With deep elation, we return "home."

It is a common religious belief that everyone's life belongs to God. We are temples of the Holy Spirit. God works WITH us as we journey through life. Together we are co-creators in this world. Our mission is to advance love. If God is love the more we love, the bigger God gets. God is never done! Maybe God isn't changeless after all.

Death seems to be a parting of earthly souls. Their destination is a mystery. There's widespread belief that there's no concept of time in the afterlife. All existence takes place in the present moment. If this is so, then when we die, everyone we're leaving here on earth is already where we are going! Mind-boggling.

(41)

THE SPACE BETWEEN EXTREMES

During a depression support group I lead, a discussion arose regarding what people missed the most due to their illness. The following were some replies:

- ✓ feeling passionate about something
- ✓ the desire or ability to smile
- ✓ connecting with others
- ✓ laughing
- ✓ I want to feel joy again!

"I want to feel joy again!" The cry was desperate and heartbreaking.

Just what exactly constitutes joy for people? I think it can be a very personal thing. Adding something positive to a person's life could be joyous. Taking something away from a person's life could also bring joy. But to a person who suffers depression and/or mood swings **joy** can be found **in the space between extremes**.

I used to think joy was defined as being so happy you wanted to jump up and down. After dealing with extreme highs and lows, I embrace the above description of joy.

When everything feels on an even keel, and a sense of balance permeates my being, my newest found love is JOY!

The space between extremes can be my heaven on earth.

"If you want to build a ship, don't drum up people to collect wood and don't assign them tasks and work, but rather teach them to long for the endless immensity of the sea."

- Antoine de Saint Exupery

(42)

GENTLE MESSAGE

"Moment by moment, one can bear much." (St. Teresa of Avila) [25]

When you feel like you just can't go on, that life is more than you can bear, repeat this mantra. It is soothing and will subdue a frantic mind. It can dispel thoughts of imagined, futuristic tragedy. It can obliterate negative feelings about the past. Our present job, right now, is living moment to moment rather than day to day. God exists in the present. Living moment to moment, you allow God to lead you and hold you in His arms. Let Him carry you through these times of confusion and set you on solid ground.

"Moment by moment, one can bear much." A duet of strength and perseverance weave a peaceful mind. Fear has no home here. Love alone abides.

"Victory has a thousand fathers, but defeat is an orphan."

- JFK

(43)

Our Voice

Though you may be feeling negative and very hateful towards yourself, you have a job to do. Try to lift yourself out of the trenches. Depending on your degree of depression, this can be a daunting task. Somebody has to do it and that somebody is you. A well-intentioned friend, or a therapist might help but we listen to the voice we give ourselves. FIND SOMETHING GOOD TO SAY ABOUT YOURSELF EVEN IF YOU DON'T BELIEVE IT AT THE TIME.

Examples of uplifting comments are:
I have pretty hair.
I care about others.
I am a nice person.
I love and care for animals.
I take good care of my children.
I take good care of my parents.
I am a loving husband.
My eyes are very pretty.
I have a nice sense of fashion.
I am a talented knitter.

Write your remarks down. Read them when you feel your best and when you feel your worst. Read them out loud. Soak them up. Resistance will be present when you feel lousy.

Turn and face your depression. Make friends with it. Do not run away from it. It will only chase you. By reciting these positive affirmations you may be weakening your depression and inviting its demise. You're flooding your mind with positive chemicals. Let them fuel your day!

"Just keep going. No feeling is final."

- Rike

(44)

EVER PRESENT HELP

Have you ever been called an angel? How wonderful if you have! What would you say that implies? One of the things I think it describes is someone who does nice things for others, often without being asked.

As I grew up I attended Catholic schools. One Catholic teaching proclaims we each have a Guardian Angel. In the grammar school mornings we prayed aloud in unison to our precious angel:

Angel of God,

my guardian dear,

to whom God's love commits me here,

ever this day,

be at my side

to light and guard,

to rule and guide.

Our present Pope Francis, while commemorating the Feast of Guardian Angels on October 2nd, 2019, quoted from the Book of Exodus: "God promised the people of Israel I'm sending an angel before you, to guard you and bring you to the place I have prepared before you." [26]

Our angels are said to help us avoid danger on our path through life. They can be the source of good decisions and safe directions. They are strong traveling companions.

The following lists some religious beliefs about angels:

> *Catholic* - each soul, Christians and non-Christians, are assigned an angel at birth to give guidance.
>
> *Islam* - unseen beings who worship God and carry out his order.
>
> *Protestant* - Believe there are nine choirs of angels with different tasks.
>
> *Judaism* - they are representatives, reminding us that God is with us at all times.
>
> *Buddhist* - do not believe in angels. [27]

I had a wonderful encounter with a being I believe was an angel. The strength of my conviction is as strong today as it was 26 years ago. The memory still sends joyous chills up and down my spine.

I took my fourteen year old son to an 8am basketball tournament at a local school. I had been feeling very low for a few weeks. I dropped him off and went to get coffee to have in the gym. On my way to the nearby store I thought, "What am I doing? I don't feel like drinking coffee one bit! I mysteriously continued on.

I went in the door and my eyes immediately felt the stare of a small, hunched back man with a very big grin. I remember thinking, "He looks like he's expecting me!" I felt nauseous and quickly looked away. I paid for my coffee and headed for the door. This man used his crippled back to push the door open for me. I timidly said "thank you" and "have a good day." He loudly replied, "And you have a good day too, BARB."

I couldn't believe it! I dropped my large coffee. I'd never seen or met this man before. The sound of my name just lifted my spirits immensely. I went on to have a terrific day. I felt in my very bones that he was an angel. I always will.

Part of my depression at the time was a feeling of insignificance and the recognition of my name made my heart soar.

There truly are angels among us. If you believe it.....you will see it.

"Everything will be okay in the end.
If it's not okay, it's not the end."

- John Lennon

(45)

ETERNITY IS NOW

I am privileged to teach on the Behavioral Units at the hospital where I work. The patients on one particular floor are dealing with depression that accompanies addiction. We often engage in discussions about the concept of time--.time as an enemy when it won't pass fast enough and friendly time when everything's going our way.

Did you know that, as far as scientists know, "time" is a concept exclusive to earth? There is no measurement of it after death. Theories tell us that eternity welcomes us when we depart. And just what is eternity?

Believe it or not, you have all visited eternity at some time in your life. Whenever you were in a situation where you did not keep track of the time concepts of before, during and after, you were in eternity. It accompanies pleasure. It is pleasure.

For instance, you might have been at a party. You looked at your phone and four hours had passed. You thought, "Holy cow, I can't believe it's that late." You were in eternity.

Eternity is not a home to pain. Once we take notice that pain exists we begin to measure it just by being aware of it. "When will this ever be over?" we ask ourselves.

The true meaning of eternity is the good ole PRESENT MOMENT. It can be described as the absence of before, during and after. Nothing can be wrong in the present moment. When we inflict our thoughts on it, we sometimes judge our situation and we've lost this gift we call the present. We've lost the ability to just BE.

There is help for controlling our thoughts.

The Holy Spirit's job is to purify our thinking and guide us on the journey to BEING.

The Holy Spirit only exists in the present. "He" is yours for the asking. He will answer every beckoned call. If a fearful thought follows your plea IT IS NOT FROM THE HOLY SPIRIT!

Eternity is the PRESENT. Eternity is the Holy Spirit's home. He begs for company and friendship.

Eternity is OUR home. The present is a present. We need only to unwrap it to enjoy its momentary surprises.

May these surprises hold adventures where depression is an uncommon stranger.

Amen

It's often said, preachers preach what they need to hear. I dare say that could be true for most of us.

I shared these tips and teachings to not only enhance your healing, but to remind myself to never give up. Depression may attempt to darken my view, but it will never steal my vision.

It has empowered me to lovingly share my thoughts with you-my readers. As we go forward joyfully together, may we send forth the collective spirit of a sound mind.

"Let your unique awesomeness and
positive energy inspire confidence in others."

- Anonymous

A Life of Love
by Burnett Eggleston

It's hard to know just where to start
As memories unfold
And feelings stir within my heart
Of golden days of old.

A nestled farm tucked in the wood
Kept safe my early years
A loving mom so kind and good
To banish all my fears.

Her kitchen warmed with walls of pine
Made such a lovely spot
To slice some fries on which to dine
And place into the pot.

Then city life did beckon us
As to the west we rode
There were now nine Burnetts in all
To fill our new abode.

I started school so eagerly
My hand mom held so tight
And little did we know the nuns
Were in for quite a fight.

These years passed all too suddenly
As family grew and grew
A new home now was needed
For the old just wouldn't do.

So on to Chapin we did go
A mansion waiting there

And oh what joys it did behold
No memories compare.

The rooms adorned with chandeliers
The staircase never-ending
Carpet snug from wall to wall
And on the stairs ascending.

A daughter born and children wed
Within these happy days
A life of love our family led
A life of love - - all ways.

NOTES

1. Capra, Frank. *It's A Wonderful Life* [Film] Liberty Films RKO Radio Pictures, 1947

2. American Psychiatric Association, *Diagnostic and Statistical Manual of Mental Disorders* (DSM-5 5th Edition) May 18, 2013, Retrieved from http://www.medscape.com/resource/dsm-5

3. Cherry. K (Gans, S. MD). *"Color Psychology: Does it Affect Your Mood?"*, May 28, 2020, Retrieved from https://www.verywellmind.com/color-psychology-2795824

4. Gomstyn, A. *"Food for your mood: How what you eat affects your mental health"*, Retrieved from https://www.aetna.com/health-guide/food-affects-mental-health.html

5. Zeratsky, K, RD LD., *"Junk food blues: Are depression and diet related?"* Retrieved from https://www.mayoclinic.org/diseases-conditions/depression/expert-answers/depression-and-diet/faq-20058241

6. Jacobs, D. Graves, G. June 2013 "*5 Myths About Meditation.*" Prevention. pg. 56-59

7. Thich Nhat Hahn, "*The most precious gift .....bloom like flowers.*" Retrieved from https://www.goodreads.com/quotes/376161-the-most-precious-gift-we-can-offer-anyone-is-our

8. Ruiz, D.M. (1997) *The Four Agreements,* Amber-Allen Publishing pg. 63-65

9. Kelly, M. (2010) *Rediscover Catholicism*, Beacon Publishing

10. Zimmer, M.B. (1983) *The Mists of Avalon*, Alfred Knopf Publishing

11. Zeidan F. *"Brain Mechanisms Supporting Violated Expectations of Pain"*, Sept. 2015 Retrieved from https://pubmed.ncbi.nlm.nih.gov/26083664/

12. Rockwood, Kate. *"The Best Hobbies for Your Mind and Body"*. Prevention, June 19. Pgs 52-53

13. Goodheart, Annette. *Laugh Your Way to Health*. VHS Video (1985) Annette Goodheart Publishing. https://www.ebay.com.jitm

14. SCL Health Sisters of Charity in Leavenworth, Kansas *"The Real Health Benefits of Smiling and Laughing"*, June 2019, Retrieved from https://www.sclhealth.org/blog/2019/06/the-real-health-benefits-of-smiling-and-laughing/

15. Stibich, M, PhD. *"Top Reasons to Smile Everyday "*, Apr. 2, 2021 Retrieved from https://www.verywellmind.com/top-reasons-to-smile-every-day-2223755

16. Mayo Clinic staff, *"Electroconvulsive Therapy (ECT) "*,Oct, 12, 2018 Retrieved from https://www.mayoclinic.org/tests-procedures/electroconvulsive-therapy/about/pac-20393894

17. Eiseley, L. *"The Starfish Throw Adaptation"* 1969 Retrieved from https://en.wikipedia.org/wiki/The_Star_Thrower

18. Oswald, D. *"Excellence Not Perfection"* Oct. 2, 2009 Retrieved from https://hrdailyadvisor.blr.com/2009/10/02/exellence-not-perfection/

19. Quote of the Day, *"When you are truly comfortable with who you are"* Feb 5, 2016 Retrieved from https://lessonslearnedinlife.com/but-you-dont-care/

20. Croskerry P. (2010). To err is human--and let's not forget it. *CMAJ : Canadian Medical Association journal = journal de l'Association medicale canadienne, 182*(5), 524. https://doi.org/10.1503/cmaj.100270 Retrieved from https://www.ncbi.nlm.nih.gov/pmc/articles/PMC2842843/#

21. Jampolsky G. G., MD (1995) *Working With Groups on Spiritual Themes*. Prescription for Peace. Whole Person Associates, pg. 40

22. Oak, M. *"And Then I Learned the Spiritual Journey,* (2020) Retrieved from https://themindsjournal.com/learned-spiritual-journey-nothing-nice/

23. Peale, N.V. (1989) *Thought Conditioners,* Foundation for Christian

24. Merton, T. *"I shall lead you through"* Thomas Merton Quotes (2020) Retrieved from https://quotefancy.com/quote/919701

25. Theresa of Avila. *"Moment By Moment One"* Klug Lyn, "Soul Weavings – A Gathering of Woman's Prayers" Retrieved from http://www.notable-quotes.com/t/teresa_of_avila.html

26. Arocho Esteves, J. *"Guardian angels are life's traveling companions, pope says"*, Oct. 2, 2018, Retrieved from https://www.catholicnews.com/guardian-angels-are-lifes-traveling-companions-pope-says/

27. Hopler, Whitney. *"Angels According to Multiple Religions."* Learn Religions, Feb. 8, 2021, Retrieved from https://www.learnreligions.com/who-are-angels-123812

My sons and their spouses contributed favorite quotes to ponder and enjoy.

"Although no one can go back and make a brand new start, anyone can start from now and make a brand new ending"
- Carl Bard

"Joy comes to us in ordinary moments. We risk missing out when we get too busy chasing down the extraordinary"
- Brene Brown

"Fight for the things you care about, but do it in a way that will lead others to join you"
- RBG

"Make happiness a priority and be gentle with yourself in the process"
- Bronnie Ware

"Victory has a thousand fathers, but defeat is an orphan"
- JFK

"If you want to build a ship, don't drum up people to collect wood and don't assign them tasks and work, but rather teach them to long for the endless immensity of the sea"
- Antoine de Saint Exupery

"An ant on the move does more than a dozing ox"
- Lao Tzu

"Ya Gotta Believe"
- Tug McGraw

"Your task is not to seek for love, but merely to seek and find all the barriers within yourself that you have built against it."
- Rumi

Just keep going. No feeling is final."
- Rilke

"If I knew this is the last time I see you, I'd tell you I love you, and would not just assume foolishly you know it already."
- Gabriel Garcia Marquez

"The meeting of two personalities is like the contact of two chemical substances: if there is any reaction, both are transformed."
-Carl Jung

"You are the sky. Everything else-is just the weather"
- Pema Chodron

"Many people think excitement is happiness. But when you are excited, you are not peaceful. True happiness is based on peace"
- Thich Nhat Hanh

"Wisdom says we are nothing. Love says we are everything. Between these two, our life flows" -- Jack Kornfield

"Much of our spiritual life is self-acceptance, maybe all of it"
-Jack Kornfield

"A few simple tips for life: feet on the ground, head to the skies, heart open, quiet mind"
- Rasheed Ogunlaru

"Loving ourselves through the process of owning our own story is the bravest thing we can do" -- Brene Brown

"So we shall let the reader answer this question for himself: who is the happier man, he who has braved the storm of life and lived or he who has stayed securely on shore and merely existed?"
(Hunter S. Thompson)

"Everything will be okay in the end. If it's not okay, it's not the end. " (John Lennon)

"The darkest hour is just before the dawn" (Thomas Fuller)

"Emancipate yourself from mental slavery, none but ourselves can free our mind." (Bob Marley)

"The journey IS the destination, enjoy the ride" (Burnett Eggleston Jr.)

"Happiness is having a large, loving, caring, close-knit family in another city." (George Burns)

Coping with various mood swings lent itself to the creation of the following poetry:

Holy Family
Burnett Eggleston

He walked beside his child wife
The babe lay still within
A place to lay their weary heads
Not founded at the inn.

Their faith was not to falter
As they trudged on through the night
The unborn child stirring
Under stars of holy light.

The brightened sky led to a path
A peaceful manger stood
Mary bore a baby king
The Light to shine all good.

Death
Burnett Eggleston

No longer do my senses know
The gift of life you were.
To feel To touch To taste To hear
Your song of love no more.
But vision doth not leaveth
When two hearts apart are torn.
My soul now knows your presence, love
The gift of life reborn.

To My Baby
Burnett Eggleston

Precious (name)
Jewel of life
Velvet skin so fair

Cuddle tight
Within my arms
My sparkling gem
So rare.

Insight
Burnett Eggleston

Insight is a gift
developed by few
A choice to see life
from a bit wider view

It comes from experience
pleasure and pain
A renewal of self
and forever a gain.

So no matter your age
let your eyes look within
For the soul has no ending
each day to begin.

A Wedding Prayer
Burnett Eggleston

Walk with each other through the years
Keep arms ever-opened wide
And share the thoughts that keep lovers close
Of feelings held sacred inside.

Talk with each other through the years
Assume not-all there is to know
About the friend you've chosen for life
As feelings change and grow.

In the brightest and darkest of moments be there
To celebrate, comfort and hold
If silence is needed then be there too
And share in a moment of gold.

Love God together through the years
For his arms are ever-opened wide
And together the three of us will become one
Where love like no other abides.

Coming
Burnett Eggleston

Sounds of laughter
Sights of fun
Darkened clouds
Please be gone

I long for freedom
From mental pain
Forever a hope
Forever a gain

Shadows will lift
They always do
I'll be one with the rest
And laughing too

Baby Girl
Eyes of wonder
Heart of gold
Daughter of delight
Life to ponder
Hands to hold
Safety in the night.

New Baby
We waited for
This angel rare
Years of longing done

Flown from
heaven up above
Our tears of joy begun.